BATH TIME FUN

BATH TIME FUN

STEP ONE FOR WATER SAFETY AND SWIM LESSONS

A book from the
"I Can Swim Water-Friendly Series"

Written by
Barbara and Scott Helpling

ISBN (Hardback) 978-1-951332-18-1
ISBN (Paperback) 978-1-951332-17-4
ISBN (eBook) 978-1-951332-19-8

All characters and events are products of the author's imagination, and any resemblance
to actual events, places or persons, living or dead is entirely coincidental.

This book is for entertainment purposes only. The author/publisher does
not have any liability to the reader or their family. Please be responsible
around water, never leave a child unattended in or around water.

Simcof Publishing®
www.simcofpublishing.com

This book belongs to:

_____

Mommy and Daddy are so
proud of their new baby.

They love playing with their new baby.
After playtime it is time for
Mommy to feed the baby.

It is bath time-before sleep time!

Daddy plays with baby while
Mommy prepares the baby
tub to give Taylor a bath.

During baths,
Mommy gently
sprinkles water
over Taylor's
head and face.

This teaches
Taylor not to be
afraid of water.

Because Mommy and Daddy make it fun, Taylor loves baths and cannot wait for bath time.

Mommy and Daddy are so happy that Taylor is not afraid of the water.

Baby Taylor is 8 months old and can now take a bath in a big tub.

Taylor sits in the tub, smiles, splashes and now wants longer baths.

Daddy claps and cheers while Taylor has fun in the bath.

Taylor loves it when mommy and daddy cheer and clap.

13

Face in the water, legs kicking,
Taylor splashes and swims in the tub.

Although 1 year old, Taylor is not
old enough to take a bath alone
and must be supervised for safety.
This is a happy time for Taylor.

16

Water is Fun!

17

Kicking, splashing, holding the breath with face in the water are fun and important skills to learn to be safe in and around the water. These are also skills needed to learn to swim.

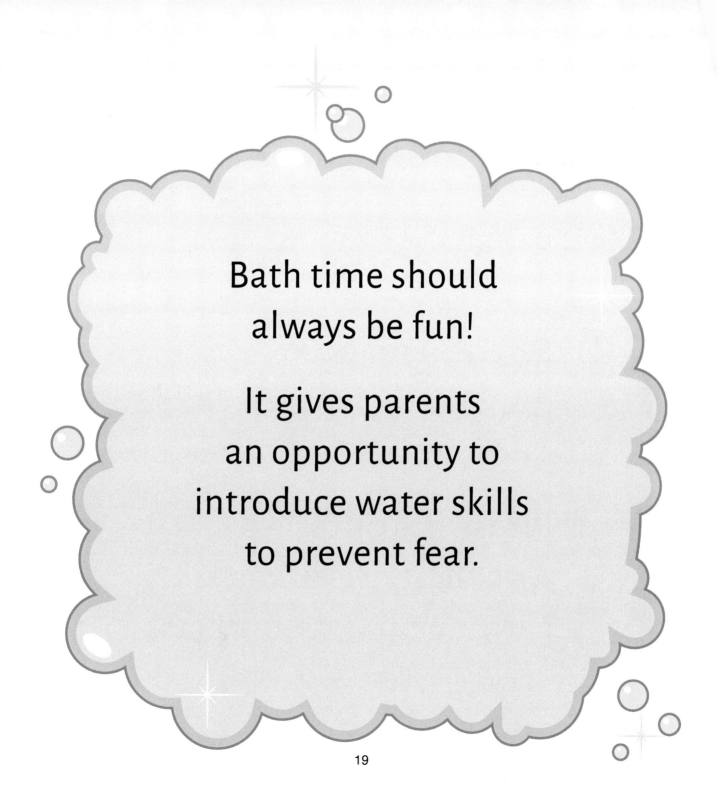

Bath time should
always be fun!

It gives parents
an opportunity to
introduce water skills
to prevent fear.

Tips for parents:

1. Parents are 100% responsible for their child's safety in and around water.

2. Please be concerned with ALL types of water: bathtubs, toilets, buckets,

hot tubs, lakes, ponds, pools, beaches, water attractions, etc.

3. Be cautious when allowing your child to visit friends and places that have water areas of concern.

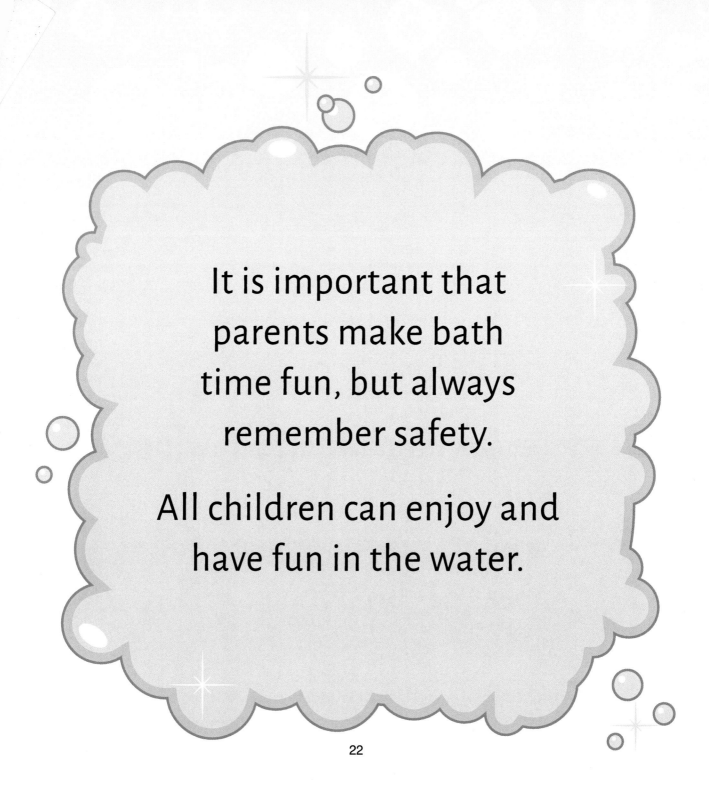

It is important that parents make bath time fun, but always remember safety.

All children can enjoy and have fun in the water.

Notes

Notes

_____

_____

_____

_____

_____

_____

Made in the USA
Columbia, SC
11 February 2021